AF271047

I LOVE FOOD...

WRITTEN BY IMAN ASHANTI
ILLUSTRATED BY TAY HILL

Confessions Publishing is a subsidiary of Roszien Kay LLC, Lancaster, CA 93536
For information regarding discounts on bulk purchase and all other inquiries, please contact the author directly at authorimanb@gmail.com.

TO MY FAMILY, FREINDS AND ALL OF MY LOVED ONES WHO
HELPED THIS PICKY EATER FALL IN LOVE WITH FOOD....
ESPECIALLY TO MY PICKY
BABIES WHOM I SEE MYSELF IN...

NOAH
TAYLOR
CHRISTIAN
NAOMI
LUCAS

THIS BOOK IS DEDICATED TO ALL FOOD EATERS...

PICKY EATERS
HAPPY EATERS
MAD EATERS
SILLY EATERS
ADVENTUROUS EATERS
FRIENDLY EATERS
FAMILY EATERS
WEIRD EATERS

AND EVERY OTHER KIND IN BETWEEN.

MAY FOOD ALWAYS BRING HAPPINESS, LOVE AND NEW

EXPERIENCES TO YOUR LIFE.

TRY EVERYTHING AT LEAST ONCE... MAYBE TWICE.

ENJOY FOOD WITH OTHERS.

ALWAYS REMEMBER HOW YOUR FAVORITE FOOD MAKES YOU FEEL...

AND LIVE THAT WAY.

I LOVE FOOD BECAUSE...

....YOU CAN SHARE.

I LOVE FOOD BECAUSE...

ON A WALK

...YOU CAN EAT ANYWHERE.

I LOVE FOOD BECAUSE...

*WHAT ARE YOUR
FAVORITE
TOPPINGS?*

EAT FOOD EXACTLY HOW YOU WANT TO EAT IT

...I CAN MAKE IT JUST FOR ME.

I LOVE FOOD BECAUSE...

...IT BRINGS TOGETHER MY FAMILY.

*PEANUT BUTTER AND BANANA SANDWICH *

I LOVE FOOD BECAUSE...

*ICE CREAM AND FRENCH FRIES *

...WEIRD CAN TASTE YUMMY.

I LOVE FOOD BECAUSE...

* WE'RE MAKING
PANCAKES! *

...I CAN HELP COOK
WITH MOMMY.

BUT... THE BEST PART
ABOUT FOOD?

...IT FILLS UP MY TUMMY!!!

RECIPES TO
COOK
TOGETHER
AND
ENJOY!

ALWAYS BE SAFE WHILE IN THE KICTHEN AND COOKING!

ALWAYS REMEBER KNIVES ARE SHARP, UNCOOKED MEAT IS YUCKY AND FIRE IS HOT.

ALWAYS LISTEN TO YOUR PARENT'S DIRECTIONS!

ALWAYS MAKE RECIPES YOUR OWN. FEEL FREE TO ADD IN ANYTHING YOU LOVE AND LEAVE OUT WHATEVER YOU DON'T.

YOUR FOOD, YOUR TASTE BUDS, YOUR TUMMY!

PANCAKES

WHIPCREAM ON TOP OR BUTTER?

* ADD IN CHOCOLATE CHIPS! TASTE GREAT! *

1 CUP	MILK
2 TBSP.	MELTED BUTTER
1	EGG BEATEN
1 CUP	FLOUR
2 TSP.	BAKING POWDER
1 1/2 TBSP.	SUGAR
1/2 TSP.	SALT
1 TBSP.	VANILLA EXTRACT
2 TBSP.	BUTTER

1. MIX THE DRY INGREDIENTS TOGETHER INTO A BOWL.

2. MIX THE EGG, MILK, BUTTER, AND VANILLA.

3. ADD TO DRY INGREDIENTS.

4. BEAT TOGETHER UNTIL SMOOTHE.

5. HEAT UP SKILLET AND GREASE IT WITH BUTTER.

6. ONCE SKILLET AT LOW/MEDIUM HEAT DROP THE BATTER IN THE SIZE OF THE PANCAKES YOU WANT (MY FAVORITE ARE LITTLE ONES)

7. COOK UNTIL THE TOP BUBBLES!

8. FLIP AND COOK OTHER SIDE TIL BROWNED HOW YOU LIKE IT. ENJOY!

GRILLED CHEESE

TRY WITH TOMATO SOUP!

2 SLICES	BREAD OF CHOICE
1 SLICE	CHEESE OF CHOICE
2 TBSP.	BUTTER

1. HEAT SKILLET TO LOW/MEDIUM HEAT AND GREASE WITH BUTTER.

2. PLACE ONE SLICE OF BREAD IN SKILLET AND THEN THE SLICE OF CHEESE ON TOP. LET COOK.

3. ONCE CHEESE BEGINS TO MELT AND BREAD BEGINS TO BROWN PLACE SECOND SLICE ON TOP.

4. BUTTER THE BREAD SLICE ON TOP AND THEN FLIP.

5. PRESS TOGETHER WITH SPATULA, COOK UNTIL BROWNED TO HOW EVERY YOU LIKE. ENJOY!

CHICKEN NOODLE SOUP

2-3 POUND	CHICKEN LEGS
10 CUPS	WATER
2 CUBES	CHICKEN BOUILLON
1 CUP	ONIONS (CHOPPED)
1/2 TSP.	SALT
1/2 TSP.	PEPPER
1	BAY LEAF
1 CUP	CELERY (SLICED)
1 CUP	CARROTS (THINLY SLICED)
2 CUPS	WIDE EGG NOODLES

1. PUT WATER AND CHICKEN IN A POT AND BRING TO BOIL. REDUCE HEAT, COVER AND SIMMER FOR 15 MINUTES.

2. ADD BOUILLON CUBES, SALT, PEPPER, AND BAY LEAF TO POT. CONTINUE TO SIMMER FOR 30 MINUTES.

3. STIR IN CELERY, CARROTS AND ONIONS. SIMMER AND COOK FOR 15MINUTES.

4. REMOVE BAY LEAF.

5. PUT NOODLES INTO BOILING SOUP AND COOK FOR 5 TO 10 MINUTES. ENJOY!

CHOCOLATE CHIP COOKIES

* GOES GREAT WITH ANY
TYPE OF
CHOCOLATE CHIP OR
ADD IN! *

1/2 CUP	MELTED BUTTER
1/3 CUP	SUGAR
1/2 CUP	LIGHT BROWN SUGAR
1	LARGE EGG
1 TSP.	VANILLA EXTRACT
1/2 TSP.	BAKING SODA
1/2 TSP.	SALT
1 1/2 CUPS	ALL-PURPOSE FLOUR
1 1/2 CUPS	MILK CHOCOLATE CHIPS

1. MIX MELTED BUTTER, SUGAR AND BROWN SUGAR TOGETHER IN LARGE BOWL UNTIL SMOOTH.

2. MIX IN EGG AND VANILLA UNTIL COMBINED.

3. MIX IN BAKING SODA AND SALT, THEN SLOWLY ADD IN FLOUR AND CONTINUE TO MIX UNTIL BATTER IS SMOOTH AND EVERYTHING IS TOGETHER.

4. SLOWLY MIX IN CHOCOLATE CHIPS MAKING SURE TO SCRAPE SIDES TO GET ALL PARTS OF BATTER.

5. SCOOP BALLS OF COOKIE DOUGH ONTO A ALUMINUM FOIL LINED COOKIE SHEET UNTIL FULL (BE SURE TO GIVE THEM SPACE). CHILL IN FRIDGE FOR AT LEAST 2 HOURS.

6. PREHEAT OVEN TO 350F. COOK UNTIL LIGHT GOLDEN BROWN. LET COOK FOR 10 MINUTES AND ENJOY!

After being born in Pacoima, California and then raised in Decatur, Georgia, I have been lucky enough to experience many different foods. My family aren't only "foodies" but they also love to travel, so I've seen about everything you can think of, majority that I didn't eat until I realized all the joys of food. I was the pickiest eater... it was bad! But, by being around my family and those that I love, I was able to see how much they loved food. They spoke with me about it, what it meant to them, told jokes and argued what was best... thinking I didn't really care... but little did they know, it meant the most to me. By showing me that food holds new experiences, friendships, unforgettable memories, our history, fun, comfort and most of all LOVE, I was able to break that picky eater mindset. I started to embrace that it doesn't hurt to try everything at least once.. or maybe twice. I hope that this book encourages you to embrace that as well and maybe fall a little more in love with food too!

#IMJUSTHERETOMAKEYOUHUNGRY

Instagram: @Imanashanti
Yelp Elite: Iman B.
Email : authorimanb@Gmail.com

CPSIA information can be obtained
at www.ICGtesting.com
Printed in the USA
BVHW021803200919
558937BV00003B/3/P